MEGAWORDS 5

2nd Edition

Decoding, Spelling, and Understanding
Multisyllabic Words

Kristin Johnson • Polly Bayrd

5 **VOWEL VARIATIONS**

School Specialty, Inc.

Cambridge and Toronto

Editorial Project Manager: Sethany Rancier Alongi
Editors: Will Tripp and Marcy Gilbert

Printed in Mayfield, PA, in December 2009
ISBN 978-0-8388-0908-2

1 2 3 4 5 6 PAH 13 12 11 10 09

Contents

To the Student

Megawords 5: Decoding, Spelling, and Understanding Multisyllabic Words is the fifth in a series of books designed to help you read and spell words that contain two or more syllables. The lists are organized according to spelling patterns and word structure. Worksheets following each list explain and help you practice the rules or patterns found in that particular group of words. Some exercises focus on reading the words; others focus on spelling or vocabulary.

Megawords is designed to meet your individual learning needs. You and your teacher can decide which lists you need to study (and which you already know) by interpreting your results on the Check Test. You may need to focus on reading and spelling. Or you may need to use **Megawords** only to improve spelling skills. You and your teacher can record your progress on the Accuracy Checklist at the back of your book.

We feel that it is important for you to be able to 1) sound out the words and 2) learn to read them proficiently and fluently. You and your teacher will set a reading rate goal. When you can read the words easily and automatically, you will be less likely to forget the words and you can concentrate on reading for meaning instead of on sounding out words. You can keep track of your reading rate on the Word Proficiency Graph at the back of your book. We also feel it is important for you to practice reading the words in connected text. At the end of each lesson is a reading passage that incorporates both list words and review words. In addition to building your comprehension, you can do repeated readings of this passage and chart your fluency rate on the Fluency Graph.

Megawords 5 introduces the vowel sounds of *y* and vowel combinations such as *ai, ow, ea,* and *eigh,* which are found in multisyllabic words. Many of these vowel combinations are already familiar to you from your knowledge of one-syllable words. However, you may find these vowel combinations quite frustrating to read and spell. A vowel combination can be pronounced as many as three different ways. And there may be four or more different ways to spell a single vowel sound. **Megawords 5** presents the vowel patterns clearly and provides plenty of practice. And as we have done in the other books in the **Megawords** series, we have included one-syllable warm-up pages to better prepare you for working with the multisyllabic words on each list.

A very important rule for word groups like this is, "Be flexible!" If the first pronunciation you try doesn't result in a word you recognize, try the next most logical pronunciation. If one spelling doesn't look right, try the next most logical way. The Vowel Combination Patterns chart on page 78 is helpful.

We hope that you will be interested in checking out your skills in reading and spelling multisyllabic words—in seeing what you know and what you need to learn. In addition, we hope that you will enjoy tackling new word groups and mastering them. We think that multisyllabic words, when presented clearly and in patterned groups, can be challenging and fun. We sincerely hope that you enjoy and experience success with **Megawords.**

—Polly Bayrd and Kristin Johnson

WORD LIST 26 — Vowel Combinations with *o*

oo = /o͞o/	ou = /o͞o/	ow, oa = /ō/	ow, ou = /ow/	oy, oi = /oi/	ou = /ə/
afternoon	acoustic	approach	account	annoy	enormous
baboon	bouquet	borrow	allow	appoint	famous
balloon	caribou	charcoal	announce	avoid	generous
caboose	cougar	cocoa	around	*boisterous	marvelous
cartoon	routine	elbow	astound	boycott	nervous
cocoon	souvenir	fellow	compound	corduroy	numerous
foolish	uncouth	follow	council	destroy	
kangaroo		hollow	counter	embroider	
lagoon		marshmallow	county	employ	
maroon		meadow	discount	enjoy	
monsoon		minnow	drowsy	exploit	
mushroom		narrow	flounder	loyal	
platoon		oatmeal	flower	moisture	
poodle		pillow	fountain	ointment	
raccoon		reproach	lousy	oyster	
shampoo		shadow	mountain	poison	
typhoon		shallow	powder	rejoice	
		sparrow	power	royal	
		tomorrow	profound	sirloin	
		willow	pronounce	turmoil	
		window	rowdy	turquoise	
		yellow	scoundrel	voyage	

ou = /ŭ/

country
couple
cousin
double
trouble

(ow, ou = /ow/ column continued:)
surround
thousand
towel
tower
trousers
vowel

*The word *boisterous* also contains the vowel combination *ou* = /ə/.

Vowel Combinations with *o*

Six vowel combinations start with *o*. Some of the combinations make more than one sound. Some of the sounds are spelled by more than one combination.

oa says /ō/ as in *road*

ow says /ō/ and /ow/ as in *bowl* and *gown*

oi says /oi/ as in *coin*

oy says /oi/ as in *joy*

oo says /o͞o/ as in *food*

ou says /ow/, /ə/, /ŭ/, and /o͞o/ as in *mouse, touch,* and *you*

(1) Read these words aloud. Practice saying the correct vowel combination with *o*.

oa says /ō/	*ow* says /ō/ or /ow/	*oi* says /oi/
boat	own	soil
oak	snow	join
goal	down	noise
toast	now	void
loan	vow	foil

oy says /oi/	*oo* says /o͞o/	*ou* says /ow/, /ŭ/, or /o͞o/
boy	goof	house
coy	boot	sour
ploy	mood	tough
soy	soon	rough
toy	roost	youth

(2) Spell the six vowel combinations with *o*.

_____ _____ _____ _____ _____ _____

Use the chart to study the different sounds vowel combinations with *o* can make.

Sounds

Vowel Combinations	/ō/	/ow/	/oi/	/ə/, /ŭ/	/o͞o/
oa	charcoal				
ow	follow	drowsy			
oi			rejoice		
oy			enjoy		
oo					foolish
ou		around		nervous, country	bouquet

(1) Circle the vowel combination with *o* in each word. Circle the sound(s) each combination can make.

f a m o u s	/ō/ /ow/ /oi/ /ə/ /o͞o/	f o o l i s h	/ō/ /ow/ /oi/ /ə/ /o͞o/
o a t m e a l	/ō/ /ow/ /oi/ /ə/ /o͞o/	p o w e r	/ō/ /ow/ /oi/ /ə/ /o͞o/
b o u q u e t	/ō/ /ow/ /oi/ /ə/ /o͞o/	r e j o i c e	/ō/ /ow/ /oi/ /ə/ /o͞o/
a n n o y	/ō/ /ow/ /oi/ /ə/ /o͞o/	c h a r c o a l	/ō/ /ow/ /oi/ /ə/ /o͞o/
d i s c o u n t	/ō/ /ow/ /oi/ /ə/ /o͞o/	m o n s o o n	/ō/ /ow/ /oi/ /ə/ /o͞o/
f o l l o w	/ō/ /ow/ /oi/ /ə/ /o͞o/	n u m e r o u s	/ō/ /ow/ /oi/ /ə/ /o͞o/

(2) Fill in each blank with the correct sample word from the chart.

oy says /oi/ as in _____   *oi* says /oi/ as in _____

ou says /ə/ as in _____   *ou* says /ow/ as in _____

ow says /ow/ as in _____   *ow* says /ō/ as in _____

ou says /o͞o/ as in _____   *oa* says /ō/ as in _____

oo says /o͞o/ as in _____   *ou* says /ŭ/ as in _____

In working with vowel combinations, it is important to be flexible. Often a vowel sound can be spelled more than one way. First, learn the different ways a vowel sound can be spelled. Then if one spelling doesn't look right in a word, try another.

(1) Circle the vowel combinations with *o* that say /o͞o/.

| balloon | souvenir | raccoon | bouquet |
| monsoon | lagoon | uncouth | acoustic |

Two ways to spell /o͞o/ are _____ and _____.

(2) Circle the vowel combinations with *o* that say /ow/.

| flower | mountain | vowel | council |
| towel | discount | account | drowsy |

Two ways to spell /ow/ are _____ and _____.

(3) Circle the vowel combinations with *o* that say /oi/.

| poison | moisture | exploit | loyal |
| oyster | voyage | employ | embroider |

Two ways to spell /oi/ are _____ and _____.

(4) Circle the vowel combinations with *o* that say /ō/.

| shallow | oatmeal | approach | cocoa |
| meadow | minnow | marshmallow | charcoal |

Two ways to spell /ō/ are _____ and _____.

① Say each syllable, and then read the whole word. Underline the vowel combination with *o* in the whole word.

ow and *oa* = /ō/

shal low	s h a l l o w
mead ow	m e a d o w
min now	m i n n o w
pil low	p i l l o w
to mor row	t o m o r r o w
marsh mal low	m a r s h m a l l o w
re proach	r e p r o a c h
co coa	c o c o a
ap proach	a p p r o a c h
char coal	c h a r c o a l

ow and *ou* = /ow/

drow sy	d r o w s y
tow el	t o w e l
vow el	v o w e l
lou sy	l o u s y
coun cil	c o u n c i l
pro found	p r o f o u n d
foun tain	f o u n t a i n
trou sers	t r o u s e r s
an nounce	a n n o u n c e
sur round	s u r r o u n d

oy and *oi* = /oi/

voy age	v o y a g e
em ploy	e m p l o y
cor du roy	c o r d u r o y
boy cott	b o y c o t t
tur quoise	t u r q u o i s e
em broi der	e m b r o i d e r
tur moil	t u r m o i l
ex ploit	e x p l o i t
a void	a v o i d

oo and *ou* = /o͞o/

bal loon	b a l l o o n
mon soon	m o n s o o n
rac coon	r a c c o o n
co coon	c o c o o n
ba boon	b a b o o n
la goon	l a g o o n
ty phoon	t y p h o o n
kan ga roo	k a n g a r o o
sou ven ir	s o u v e n i r
a cous tic	a c o u s t i c
bou quet	b o u q u e t

① Match the syllables to make real words. Say each word aloud as you write it.

mon	coon	_monsoon_
bal	boon	_____
rac	soon	_____
ba	toon	_____
pla	loon	_____

scoun	sers	_____
coun	der	_____
floun	drel	_____
lou	cil	_____
trou	sy	_____

com	count	_____
an	round	_____
dis	pound	_____
as	nounce	_____
sur	tound	_____

ex	point	_____
sir	ploit	_____
tur	joice	_____
ap	quoise	_____
re	loin	_____

② Unscramble the syllables to make real words.

row mor to	_____
em der broi	_____
mal marsh low	_____
roo kan ga	_____
noon af ter	_____
cous a tic	_____
ir sou ven	_____
roy du cor	_____
ous mar vel	_____
car bou i	_____

1   Your teacher will dictate twenty-four words. Spell the missing syllable, using the hints at the left. Then say the whole word as you write it.

/ow/—spelled *ou*

1. _____ tain   _____

2. a _____   _____

3. dis _____   _____

/ow/—spelled *ow*

4. _____ er   _____

5. al _____   _____

6. _____ er   _____

/oi/—spelled *oi*

7. oint _____   _____

8. _____ ter   ous   _____

9. _____ ture   _____

/oi/—spelled *oy*

10. _____ al   _____

11. em _____   _____

12. voy _____   _____

/ō/—spelled *oa*

13. _____ meal   _____

14. char _____   _____

15. ap _____   _____

/ō/—spelled *ow*

16. yel _____   _____

17. win _____   _____

18. to   mor _____   _____

/o͞o/—spelled *oo*

19. sham _____   _____

20. car _____   _____

21. af   ter _____   _____

/o͞o/—spelled *ou*

22. _____ ve   nir   _____

23. _____ tine   _____

24. _____ gar   _____

S Review

VC/CV When two or more consonants stand between two vowels, divide between the consonants so that blends and digraphs stay together.

/Cle Divide before the Consonant-*le*.

V/CV When a single consonant is surrounded by two vowels, the most common division is before the consonant, making the vowel in the first syllable long. In some words, the first syllable is unaccented and has a schwa sound instead of a long-vowel sound.

VV/ When a vowel combination appears at the end of a syllable, divide right after the vowel combination.

(1) Divide these words into syllables using the VC/CV rule. Draw a box around the accented syllable.

el|bow	oatmeal	employ
account	borrow	shampoo

(2) Divide these words into syllables using the /Cle rule. Draw a box around the accented syllable.

trouble   couple   poodle

(3) Divide these words into syllables using the V/CV rule. Draw a box around the accented syllable.

famous	cocoa	cocoon
around	lagoon	avoid

(4) Divide these words into syllables using the VV/ rule. Draw a box around the accented syllable.

flower	royal	power
loyal	voyage	rowdy

ou

The vowel combination *ou* has several different sounds in multisyllabic words:

ou usually says /ow/ as in *around*.

ou can say /ə/ as in *famous* or /ŭ/ as in *cousin*.

ou can say /o͞o/ as in *routine*.

If you read an *ou* word you do not know, sound it out, first with *ou* saying /ow/, then /ə/ or /ŭ/, and then /o͞o/, until you hear a word you recognize.

1 Divide these words into syllables. Then write them under the correct headings.

a|round   famous   counter   double   discount

couple   trouble   thousand   nervous   cougar

bouquet   caribou   account   routine   souvenir

ou says /ow/   **ou says /ə/ or /ŭ/**   **ou says /o͞o/**

around

2 **EXCEPTION** The word *shoulder* doesn't fit into any of these categories. Instead, *shoulder* says /ō/. Fill in the blanks to practice spelling this exception.

shoulder   sh_____lder   shoul_____

_____oul_____   _____der   _____

Review

Review these accent patterns.

The accent is usually on the first syllable in two- and three-syllable words.

The accent is usually on the root (the second syllable) in words that contain a prefix and a root.

ow

The vowel combination *ow* at the end of a word usually says /ō/ as in *window*.
At the end of any other syllable, *ow* usually says /ow/ as in *flower*.

(1) Write each word under the correct heading.

| drowsy | shallow | power | yellow | shadow | minnow |
| tower | rowdy | elbow | powder | hollow | towel |

ow says /ō/ as in *window*

_____

_____

_____

_____

_____

_____

ow says /ow/ as in *flower*

_____

_____

_____

_____

_____

_____

(2) Fill in the missing vowel combinations.

Sounds

Vowel Combinations	/ō/	/ow/	/oi/	/ə/, /ŭ/	/ōō/
__ __	cocoa				
__ __	window	flower			
__ __			poison		
__ __			royal		
__ __					balloon
__ __		mountain		famous cousin	acoustic

Many words that say /o͞o/ end in *oon*. The accent is always on the final *oon* syllable.

1 **Fill in the missing letters to make a word from the box. Then write the whole word.**

| baboon | raccoon | cocoon | maroon | afternoon |
| lagoon | balloon | platoon | typhoon | cartoon |

a silky pod made by a caterpillar _____coon _____

a type of large monkey _____boon _____

an animal with a ringed tail
and masked face _____coon _____

a bag that floats away when
filled with air _____loon _____

a funny drawing _____toon _____

a pond connected with a larger
body of water _____goon _____

a group of soldiers _____toon _____

to leave stranded _____roon _____

a violent storm _____phoon _____

the time from noon
until evening _____ _____noon _____

2 **QUICK CHECK** Have another student test you on spelling these words.

My score: ___ /___ words correct

Review

When *ow* is at the end of a word, it usually says /ō/.

(1) Read the definitions. Choose the correct word from the box, and write it on the line.

willow	meadow	elbow	follow
hollow	narrow	shallow	tomorrow
shadow	yellow	fellow	minnow

a dark image made by something in the sun   _____

low, grassy land   _____

the day after today   _____

the joint between the upper and lower arm   _____

a color   _____

come after; go after   _____

a small fish   _____

having nothing inside; empty   _____

not deep   _____

a man   _____

not wide   _____

a type of tree   _____

Six of these words end with the same four letters: __ __ __ __

(2) **QUICK CHECK** Have another student test you on spelling these words.

My score: _____ /_____ words correct

/oi/

The vowel combinations *oi* and *oy* both say /oi/.

- If /oi/ is in the middle or at the beginning of a syllable, it is usually spelled *oi*, as in *poin ted* or *oint ment*. You will hear a consonant after /oi/.

- If /oi/ is at the end of a syllable, it is usually spelled *oy*, as in *roy al*.

① Your teacher will dictate six words with /oi/. Repeat each syllable, and write the word under the correct heading.

oi		*oy*
_____	_____	_____
_____	_____	_____

/ow/

The vowel combinations *ou* and *ow* both say /ow/.

- If /ow/ is in the middle of a syllable, it is usually spelled *ou*, as in *moun tain*. You will hear a consonant after /ow/.

- If /ow/ is at the end of a syllable, it is usually spelled *ow*, as in *flow er*.

② Your teacher will dictate six words with /ow/. Repeat each syllable, and write the word under the correct heading.

ou		*ow*
_____	_____	_____
_____	_____	_____

③ Fill in the blanks with the correct vowel combination and sound.

	Vowel Combination	Sound		Example
1.	_____ says	/_____/	as in	*cougar.*
2.	_____ says	/_____/	as in	*shampoo.*
3.	_____ says	/_____/	as in	*window.*
4.	_____ says	/_____/	as in	*oatmeal.*
5.	_____ says	/_____/	as in	*trouble.*

1 **Read the definitions. Choose the correct word from the box, and write it on the line.**

exploit	rowdy	discount	bouquet
tomorrow	drowsy	rejoice	embroider
uncouth	sparrow	boycott	corduroy

an arrangement of flowers in a bunch _____

the amount taken off a price _____

a thick, cotton cloth with velvety ridges _____

a bold, unusual act; to take advantage of _____

to avoid; to refuse to buy or use _____

to sew an ornamental design on cloth _____

awkward; crude; unpleasant _____

noisy _____

sleepy; half-asleep _____

to feel great joy _____

the day after today _____

a common small bird _____

Proofreading Practice

Two of the List 26 words are misspelled in each sentence. Rewrite the whole sentence, and spell the words correctly.

1. If I had a thowsand dollars in my account, I would buy a fountin.

   _____

   _____

2. There is a sparroe on the willow tree near the water touer.

   _____

   _____

3. Ms. Carter reprowched the scoandrel for crushing her flowers.

   _____

   _____

4. Moya had a marvelus dinner of flounder, oisters, and mushrooms.

   _____

   _____

5. All this moysture will allow us to duble the number of crops we grow.

   _____

   _____

6. The bride, surrownded by friends, said that she would throw her booquet.

   _____

   _____

7. In the afternoun, we should take a trip to the meadou out in the country.

   _____

   _____

8. I find it hard to enjoi boisterous parties, and that is why I avoyd them.

   _____

   _____

(1) **Read the sentences and circle all the List 26 words.**

1. Ms. Price was thrilled to see a meadow full of flowers outside her window.

2. I will no doubt hear a reproach if I don't clean the fountain.

3. Ms. Hunt enjoyed the sirloin steak she cooked on her charcoal grill.

4. On close examination, Lisa spotted several minnows in the lagoon.

5. Tony will be in trouble if he forgets to buy oatmeal tomorrow.

6. Jen was surrounded by kangaroos when she went to Australia.

7. Henry wiped the moisture off the window with a towel.

8. Let's put some cocoa butter ointment on your elbow.

9. We will appoint Mr. Turner to the county council tomorrow.

10. We caught a giant flounder yesterday afternoon.

11. My famous cousin sometimes wears turquoise corduroy trousers.

(2) **Your teacher will dictate three of the sentences above. Write them on a blank piece of paper.**

(3) **Write a short story or descriptive paragraph using ten words from List 26. Be creative!**

✔ Reading & Spelling Skill Check

Demonstrate your accuracy in reading and spelling List 26 words. Your teacher will select ten words to read and ten words to spell. Record your scores on the Accuracy Checklist. Work toward 90–100 percent accuracy.

Word Proficiency

Now build up your reading proficiency with List 26 words. Decide on your rate goal with your teacher. Record your progress on the Word Proficiency Graph.

My goal for reading List 26 is _____ words per minute with two or fewer errors.

(1) Practice the words, read the passage, and then answer the questions.

List 26 Words			Review Words		Passage Words
avoids	thousands	lousy	snowy	floated	minutes
trouble	around	announced	solo	inside	
marvelous	mountain	yellow	under	waited	
balloon(s)	voyage	nervously			

Calvin Avoids Trouble

"Marvelous! Just marvelous!" said Calvin, as he looked up at the balloon over his head. He was in the basket of a hot air balloon, thousands of feet in the sky. All around him he could see snowy mountain peaks. Calvin was halfway through his solo voyage around the world, but he sensed some trouble.

"The lousy thing is leaking air," he announced to the still sky. If the balloon did have a leak, Calvin's voyage would be cut short. Worse, he could end up lost on a remote mountain.

Calvin had to test the balloon for leaks. He lit a small fire in a pot to make some yellow smoke. Then he held it under the balloon's opening. The smoke floated inside. If there were a leak, Calvin would soon see the yellow smoke flowing from it. He waited and watched nervously. Ten minutes passed with no sign of smoke.

"Marvelous!" he said again. "The voyage goes on."

1. Which word from the text means "long trip"? _____

2. What is Calvin doing? _____

   _____

3. How does he find out that there is no leak? _____

   _____

(2) **FLUENCY** Record your progress on the Fluency Graph.

My goal for reading the passage is _____ words per minute with two or fewer errors.

ai, ay = /ā/	*au* = /aw/	*augh, aw* = /aw/	*al, all* = /all/	*al* = /ăl/
acquaint	applause	awesome	almanac	Alabama
afraid	astronaut	awful	already	Albert
ailment	auction	awkward	alter	album
appraise	audible	awning	alternate	alcove
attain	audience	coleslaw	although	Alexander
betray	auditorium	daughter	always	Alfred
campaign	auditory	dawdle	asphalt	Alice
complain	augment	distraught	enthrall	Allen
crayon	August	haughty	recall	allergy
daisy	austere	naughty	wallet	alley
delay	Australia	outlaw	walnut	alligator
detail	authentic	rawhide	walrus	allocate
detain	author	sawdust	Walter	alphabet
display	authorize	strawberry		altitude
entertain	autobiography	unlawful		halibut
essay	autograph	withdraw		malpractice
maintain	automatic			
mayor	automobile			
mislaid	autumn			
obtain	auxiliary			
proclaim	because			
relay	caucus			
remainder	cauliflower			
restrain	caustic			
retain	caution			
subway	gaudy			
sustain	laundry			
terrain	nautical			
traitor	saucer			
waitress	sausage			
	somersault			

Vowel Combinations with *a*

Six vowel combinations start with *a*. Some of the combinations make more than one sound. Some of the sounds are spelled by more than one combination.

ai says /ā/ as in *rain*

ay says /ā/ as in *stay*

au says /aw/ as in *pause*

augh says /aw/ as in *taught*

aw says /aw/ as in *claw*

al says /all/ and /ăl/ as in *call* and *pal*

(1) Read these words aloud. Practice saying the correct vowel combination with *a*.

ai says /ā/	*ay* says /ā/	*au* says /aw/
paint	stay	fault
train	play	cause
claim	way	haul
jail	tray	gauze
paid	gray	haunt

augh says /aw/	*aw* says /aw/	*al* or *all* says /all/ or /ăl/
caught	lawn	small
taught	jaw	tall
naught	flaw	hall
fraught	crawl	gal
aught	yawn	shall

(2) Spell the six vowel combinations with *a*.

_____   _____   _____   _____   _____   _____

Use the chart to study the different sounds vowel combinations with *a* can make.

Sounds

Vowel Combinations	/ā/	/aw/	/all/	/ăl/
ai	detail			
ay	crayon			
au		laundry		
aw		awful		
augh		daughter		
al			walnut	alphabet

① **Circle the vowel combinations with *a* that say /ā/.**

remainder	obtain	display	relay
proclaim	detail	terrain	betray
complain	delay	subway	mayor

Two ways to spell /ā/ are _____ and _____.

② **Circle the vowel combinations with *a* that say /aw/.**

daughter	rawhide	withdraw	saucer
autobiography	somersault	strawberry	haughty
naughty	author	distraught	because

Three ways to spell /aw/ are _____, _____, and _____.

① Say each syllable, and then read the whole word. Underline the vowel combination with *a* in the whole word.

ai = /ā/

com plain	complain
re strain	restrain
mis laid	mislaid
ob tain	obtain
en ter tain	entertain
re main der	remainder
at tain	attain
ap praise	appraise

ay = /ā/

may or	mayor
cray on	crayon
be tray	betray
de lay	delay
sub way	subway

al = /all/

al though	although
al read y	already
al ma nac	almanac
al ter nate	alternate

al = /ăl/

Al len	Allen
al ler gy	allergy
al pha bet	alphabet
al lo cate	allocate
al ti tude	altitude
al li ga tor	alligator

au and aw = /aw/

daw dle	dawdle
out law	outlaw
straw ber ry	strawberry
aug ment	augment
aus tere	austere
nau ti cal	nautical
caul i flow er	cauliflower
au to mo bile	automobile
au then tic	authentic

(1) Match the syllables to make real words. Say each word aloud as you write it.

mis	tain	_mislaid_	pro	strain	_____
trai	laid	_____	re	claim	_____
main	tor	_____	ter	tain	_____
ail	fraid	_____	sus	rain	_____
a	ment	_____	cam	paign	_____

awk	ing	_____	as	thrall	_____
daw	slaw	_____	wal	call	_____
sau	ward	_____	al	rus	_____
awn	sage	_____	re	ways	_____
cole	dle	_____	en	phalt	_____

(2) Unscramble the syllables to make real words.

ti cal nau	_____
then au tic	_____
der re main	_____
nac ma al	_____
er sault som	_____
tice mal prac	_____
tude al ti	_____
ter en tain	_____
ler al gy	_____

① Your teacher will dictate twenty-one words. Spell the missing syllable, using the hints at the left. Then say the whole word as you write it.

/ā/—spelled *ai*
1. _____ ment   _____

2. a _____   _____

3. re _____ der   _____

/ā/—spelled *ay*
4. _____ or   _____

5. de _____   _____

6. _____ on   _____

/ăl/—spelled *al*
7. _____ li ga tor   _____

8. _____ i but   _____

9. _____ pha bet   _____

/all/—spelled *al*
10. _____ nut   _____

11. _____ ter nate   _____

12. _____ ma nac   _____

/aw/—spelled *au*
13. be _____   _____

14. _____ dry   _____

15. _____ then tic   _____

/aw/—spelled *aw*
16. _____ hide   _____

17. out _____   _____

18. un _____ ful   _____

/aw/—spelled *augh*
19. _____ ter   _____

20. _____ ty   _____

21. _____ ty   _____

Review

VC/CV When two or more consonants stand between two vowels, divide between the consonants so that blends and digraphs stay together.

/Cle Divide right before the Consonant-*le*.

VV/ When a vowel combination appears at the end of a syllable, divide right after the vowel combination.

Compound Words Divide between the two words.

Prefix/Root/Suffix Divide between the prefix, root, and suffix (or ending).

(1) Divide these words into syllables using the VC/CV rule. Draw a box around the accented syllable.

laundry campaign essay

(2) Divide these words into syllables using the /Cle rule. Draw a box around the accented syllable.

dawdle audible

(3) Divide these words into syllables using the VV/ rule. Draw a box around the accented syllable.

haughty altitude awful

mayor crayon alley

(4) Divide these words into syllables using the compound words rule. Draw a box around the accented syllable.

withdraw sawdust rawhide

(5) Divide these words into syllables using the prefix/root/suffix rule. Draw a box around the accented syllable.

recall detain unlawful

al

The vowel combination *al* has two different sounds.

    al can say /all/ as in *always*.

    al can say /ăl/ as in *allergy*.

If you read an *al* word you do not know, sound it out, first with *al* saying /ăl/.
If that does not make a recognizable word, try saying /all/ instead.

1   **Divide these words into syllables. Then write them under the correct headings.**

a l t e r	a l t h o u g h	a l c o v e	a l b u m	A l f r e d
a l p h a b e t	a l l i g a t o r	A l b e r t	a l w a y s	a l t i t u d e
a l l e r g y	A l i c e	a l l o c a t e	a l l e y	a l r e a d y
A l l e n	a l t e r n a t e	A l e x a n d e r	A l a b a m a	a l m a n a c

al* says /all/ as in *almanac

    alter

al* says /ăl/ as in *alligator

2   **QUICK CHECK Have another student test you on spelling these words.**

My score: ____ /____ words correct

au = /aw/
When /aw/ is at the beginning of a word, it is usually spelled *au*.

(1) Fill in the missing *au,* and then write the whole word.

_____ction _____   _____gust _____

_____tumn _____   _____thor _____

_____stere _____   _____gment _____

_____stralia _____   _____xiliary _____

_____thentic _____   _____thorize _____

aw = /aw/
Sometimes /aw/ is spelled *aw* at the beginning of a word.

(2) Fill in the missing *aw,* and then write the whole word.

_____ful _____   _____kward _____

_____ning _____   _____esome _____

augh = /aw/
In some words, /aw/ is spelled *augh*.

(3) Fill in the missing *augh,* and then write the whole word.

d_____ter _____   distr_____t _____

n_____ty _____   h_____ty _____

(4) **EXCEPTION** In the word *laughter, augh* says /ăf/ instead of /aw/. Fill in the blanks to practice spelling this exception.

laughter   l_____ter   laugh_____

_____augh_____   _____ter   _____

/aw/

The vowel combinations *au* and *aw* both say /aw/.

- If /aw/ is in the middle or at the beginning of a syllable, it is usually spelled *au*, as in *laun dry*. You will hear a consonant after /aw/.
- If /aw/ is at the end of a syllable, it is usually spelled *aw*, as in *aw ful* and *out law*.

1 Your teacher will dictate nine words with /aw/. Repeat each syllable, and write the word under the correct heading.

au		aw
_____	_____	_____
_____	_____	_____
_____	_____	_____

/ā/

The vowel combinations *ai* and *ay* both make the /ā/ sound.

- If the /ā/ sound is in the middle or at the beginning of a syllable, it is usually spelled *ai*, as in *maid en*. You will hear a consonant after /ā/.
- If the /ā/ sound is at the end of a syllable, it is usually spelled *ay*, as in *de lay*.

2 Your teacher will dictate nine words with the /ā/ sound. Repeat each syllable, and write the word under the correct heading.

ai		ay
_____	_____	_____
_____	_____	_____
_____	_____	_____

Review

Two vowel combinations that say /ā/ are _____ and _____.

Three vowel combinations that say /aw/ are _____, _____, and _____.

_____ can say /all/ as in *almanac* or /ăl/ as in *alligator*.

Some words with *ai* contain the Latin root *tain*, meaning "hold."

(1) **Read the definitions. Choose the correct word from the box, and write it on the line.**

| maintain | attain | detain | entertain | retain | obtain |

to hold back; to take into custody _____

to keep in a state of good repair _____

to get something _____

to achieve a goal; to accomplish _____

to keep in possession; to hold onto _____

to amuse; to give attention to _____

Some words have a suffix after the root *tain*, as in *entertainment* or *obtainable*.
In some cases, *tain* changes to *ten* when the suffix is added.

(2) **Read these words aloud. Circle the syllable *tain* or *ten* in each word.**

retain ⟶ retention

detain ⟶ detention

maintain ⟶ maintenance

sustain ⟶ sustenance

Some words with *au* contain the Greek prefix *auto-*, meaning "self."

1 **Read the definitions. Choose the correct word from the box, and write it on the line.**

automobile   autobiography   automatic   autograph

a person's signature   _____

moving or acting by itself   _____

a motorcar   _____

the story of a person's life written by that person   _____

Some words with *au* contain the Latin root *audio*, meaning "hearing."

2 **Read the definitions. Choose the correct word from the box, and write it on the line.**

audible   auditory   auditorium   audience

loud enough to be heard   _____

people gathered to see and hear a show   _____

having to do with hearing   _____

a large room where people gather to see and hear shows _____

1 Fill in the blanks with words from the box.

authorize	obtain	applause	gaudy	alternate
dawdle	almanac	display	mayor	caution

1. Alison will have to _____ a fishing license to fish here.

2. The _____ talked to his advisers about the state of the city.

3. If you _____ in the morning, you might be late to work.

4. There was tremendous _____ after Act I.

5. The detour forced Mr. Austin to take an _____ route.

6. The museum has many beautiful artworks on _____.

7. The jeweled necklace was too _____ for my taste.

8. My sports _____ lists all major sporting events from last year.

9. Proceed with _____ through this dangerous intersection.

10. The doctor will _____ this prescription for your medicine.

2 Fill in the missing vowel combinations.

		Sounds		
	/ā/	/aw/	/all/	/ăl/
___ ___	afraid			
___ ___	essay			
___ ___		applause		
___ ___		sawdust		
___ ___ ___		haughty		
___ ___			alter	album

Vowel Combinations

1 **Read the definitions. Choose the correct word from the box, and write it on the line.**

augment	detain	altitude	nautical	asphalt
authentic	crayon	audible	austere	acquaint
proclaim	caustic	caucus		

having to do with ships, sailors, or sailing   _____

able to be heard   _____

genuine; real; not fake   _____

to make greater or stronger   _____

a tar-like substance used in pavement   _____

a stick of colored wax used for drawing   _____

to keep back, delay, or keep from going away   _____

height above the ground   _____

to declare publicly; to make known officially   _____

to make familiar   _____

stern or strict in manner or appearance   _____

able to burn or eat away chemically   _____

a meeting of political party members   _____

Proofreading Practice

Two of the List 27 words are misspelled in each sentence. Rewrite the whole sentence, and spell the words correctly.

1. Allen hated doing the lawndry becawse he found it boring.

   _____

   _____

2. Walter prepared a wallnut strauberry tart for dessert.

   _____

   _____

3. The awdience saved the most applause for the astronaut and the maior.

   _____

   _____

4. The Farmer's Allmanac predicts that we will have awful weather in Awgust.

   _____

   _____

5. Subwae construction was already behind schedule when the delai occurred.

   _____

   _____

6. The auther wrote an autobiography about his time on the campaygn trail.

   _____

   _____

7. Proceed with caution through this dangerous high-alltitude terrayne.

   _____

   _____

8. Alice is distrawt over her daughter's nauhty behavior.

   _____

   _____

(1) **Read the sentences and circle all the List 27 words.**

1. Alice's income is augmented by her side business selling strawberries.

2. Ms. Alexander, our mayor, addressed the crowd with some words of caution.

3. Albert bought an automobile at the auction.

4. Allen's allergy to smoke made him distraught.

6. Sue complained about the coleslaw but loved the cauliflower.

7. We will have to allocate more funds because we need more asphalt for a new road.

8. Walter was the author of a well-known almanac.

9. The audience gave the campaign speaker a round of applause.

10. I cooked the sausage while Alfred entertained the guests.

11. The awful traitor was detained last August.

(2) **Your teacher will dictate three of the sentences above. Write them on a blank piece of paper.**

(3) **Write a short story or descriptive paragraph using ten words from List 27. Be creative!**

✓ **Reading & Spelling Skill Check**

Demonstrate your accuracy in reading and spelling List 27 words. Your teacher will select ten words to read and ten words to spell. Record your scores on the Accuracy Checklist. Work toward 90–100 percent accuracy.

🕐 **Word Proficiency**

Now build up your reading proficiency with List 27 words. Decide on your rate goal with your teacher. Record your progress on the Word Proficiency Graph.

My goal for reading List 27 is _____ words per minute with two or fewer errors.

① Practice the words, read the passage, and then answer the questions.

List 27 Words			Review Words		Passage Words
subway	relayed	unlawful	traffic	above	city
terrain	authorize	maintained	tunnel	secret	system
delays	alternate		people		trolley
Alfred	always				corrupt

The Secret Subway of New York

In 1869, the New York City terrain was a mess of cars and traffic delays. But Alfred Beach had a plan: an underground tunnel filled with trains that relayed people back and forth. His plan would become the city's first subway system.

The city bosses would not authorize Beach to start his subway. They had plans for a trolley system above the streets. This alternate plan would make the crooked city leaders rich.

Beach was not one to heed corrupt leaders. His crew dug a 300-foot tunnel, always at night. They worked in secret for a year, and in 1870, the new subway opened. It was a huge hit!

The city bosses shut the unlawful subway down, and as time went by, no one maintained it. It was lost until 1912, when workers on a new subway dug up the old tunnel. Beach was long dead, but his secret subway made him a legend.

1. Which word from the text means "kept in good condition"? _____

2. Why did the city bosses *not* want Beach to build his subway? _____

_____

3. What did the city bosses do when Beach opened his subway? _____

_____

② **FLUENCY** Record your progress on the Fluency Graph.

My goal for reading the passage is _____ words per minute with two or fewer errors.

afternoon	awful	double	nervous
alligator	because	embroider	poison
allocate	bouquet	follow	recall
already	campaign	laundry	rejoice
alternate	council	marvelous	routine
altitude	crayon	mayor	strawberry
announce	dawdle	meadow	tomorrow
annoy	detail	moisture	tower
applause	discount	mushroom	wallet
approach	distraught	naughty	

1 Circle the vowel combination with *o* or *a* in each word.

altitude	council	alligator	double	nervous
wallet	tower	laundry	routine	annoy
crayon	follow	poison	awful	alternate
mushroom		approach		campaign

2 Fill in the missing vowel combinations.

Sounds

Vowel Combinations	/ō/	/ow/	/oi/	/ŭ/	/o͞o/
__ __	approach				
__ __	tomorrow	tower			
__ __			moisture		
__ __			annoy		
__ __					afternoon
__ __		discount		double	routine

Sounds

Vowel Combinations	/ā/	/aw/	/all/	/ăl/
__ __	detail			
__ __	mayor			
__ __		because		
__ __		dawdle		
__ __ __		naughty		
__ __			already	alligator

③ **Fill in the blanks with words from the box.**

applause	already	strawberry	tomorrow
discount	double	annoy	allocate

1. Last Sunday we had a choice of _____ or blueberry pancakes for breakfast.

2. If those children continue to _____ the dog, he may snap at them.

3. Stacy is looking forward to _____ because it is the start of soccer season.

4. You'll have to pay extra if you want a _____ scoop of ice cream instead of a single scoop.

5. Steven hoped he would get a round of _____ at the end of his solo.

6. Marta and Terry had _____ bought tickets for the concert when they heard the news that it was canceled.

7. We'll have to _____ more resources to the project if we want to finish it on time.

8. The store is offering a _____ on all major brands.

④ **Unscramble the syllables to make real words.**

af   noon   ter   _____

ter   al   nate   _____

ti   tude   al   _____

vel   ous   mar   _____

broi   der   em   _____

(5) Complete the puzzle with words from the box.

distraught	discount	nervous	council
alternate	bouquet	moisture	meadow
recall	double	announce	rejoice

Across

2. twice as many
6. to feel joy
7. a bunch of flowers
9. to declare publicly
10. water vapor
11. extremely sad or upset

Down

1. a grassy field
2. the lowering of the usual price of a product
3. an option, choice, or substitute
4. to remember
5. a group of people elected to govern a town or city
8. feeling anxious or worried

ee = /ē/	ey = /ē/	ea = /ē/	ea, ei, ey, eigh = /ā/	ea = /ĕ/	ew, eu = /o͞o/ or /ū/
asleep	alley	beaver	*beefsteak	abreast	Andrew
between	attorney	beneath	breakable	breakfast	cashew
canteen	baloney	bleachers	breakage	breathless	curfew
chimpanzee	chimney	conceal	convey	endeavor	euphemism
committee	hockey	decrease	*eighteen	feather	euphoria
degree	honey	disease	eighty	headquarters	Europe
disagree	jersey	eager	freighter	heather	feudal
discreet	jockey	eagle	greatest	heavy	jewel
employee	journey	feature	greatly	instead	Lewis
fifteen	kidney	increase	greatness	leather	maneuver
freedom	money	leader	greyhound	meadow	mildew
pedigree	monkey	meager	neighbor	measure	nephew
refugee	turkey	measles	neighborhood	pheasant	neutral
thirteen	valley	peacock	obey	pleasant	neutrality
volunteer		peanut	*reindeer	pleasure	pewter
	ei = /ē/	reason	surveillance	ready	sewer
		release	survey	steady	therapeutic
	caffeine	repeat	unveil	sweater	
	ceiling	squeamish	weightless	treachery	
	conceited	teacher		weapon	
	conceive	teapot		weather	
	deceive	treatment			
	either	treaty			
	leisure	weasel			
	neither				
	protein				
	receipt				
	receive				
	seizure				

*These words also contain the vowel combination ee = /ē/.

Vowel Combinations with *e*

Seven vowel combinations start with *e*. Some of the combinations make more than one sound. Some of the sounds are spelled by more than one combination.

ee says /ē/ as in *keep*

ey says /ē/ and /ā/ as in *key* and *hey*

ei says /ē/ and /ā/ as in *seize* and *vein*

eigh says /ā/ as in *weigh*

ea says /ē/, /ā/, and /ĕ/ as in *leap, break,* and *bread*

ew says /ōō/ and /ū/ as in *new* and *few*

eu says /ōō/ and /ū/ as in *deuce* and *feud*

① Read these words aloud. Practice saying the correct vowel combination with *e*.

ee says /ē/	*ey* says /ē/ or /ā/	*ei* says /ē/ or /ā/	*eigh* says /ā/
sleep	key	seize	eight
peel	prey	reins	sleigh
deer	they	veil	freight
feed	hey	feint	neigh

ea says /ē/, /ā/, or /ĕ/	*ew* says /ōō/ or /ū/	*eu* says /ōō/ or /ū/
team	blew	deuce
steak	flew	feud
breath	few	
health	hew	

② Spell the seven vowel combinations with *e*.

_____ _____ _____ _____

_____ _____ _____

Use the chart to study the different sounds vowel combinations with *e* can make.

Sounds

Vowel Combinations	/ē/	/ā/	/ĕ/	/o͞o/	/ū/
ee	asleep				
ea	teacher	breakable	weather		
ei	receive	unveil			
eigh		eighty			
ey	turkey	obey			
ew				jewel	curfew
eu				neutral	feudal

① Circle the vowel combination with *e* in each word. Then circle all the sound(s) each combination can make.

leader	/ē/ /ā/ /ĕ/ /o͞o/ /ū/	discreet	/ē/ /ā/ /ĕ/ /o͞o/ /ū/
cashew	/ē/ /ā/ /ĕ/ /o͞o/ /ū/	seizure	/ē/ /ā/ /ĕ/ /o͞o/ /ū/
weasel	/ē/ /ā/ /ĕ/ /o͞o/ /ū/	unveil	/ē/ /ā/ /ĕ/ /o͞o/ /ū/
feudal	/ē/ /ā/ /ĕ/ /o͞o/ /ū/	freighter	/ē/ /ā/ /ĕ/ /o͞o/ /ū/
pheasant	/ē/ /ā/ /ĕ/ /o͞o/ /ū/	pewter	/ē/ /ā/ /ĕ/ /o͞o/ /ū/
survey	/ē/ /ā/ /ĕ/ /o͞o/ /ū/	euphoria	/ē/ /ā/ /ĕ/ /o͞o/ /ū/
eager	/ē/ /ā/ /ĕ/ /o͞o/ /ū/	maneuver	/ē/ /ā/ /ĕ/ /o͞o/ /ū/
steady	/ē/ /ā/ /ĕ/ /o͞o/ /ū/	convey	/ē/ /ā/ /ĕ/ /o͞o/ /ū/
weapon	/ē/ /ā/ /ĕ/ /o͞o/ /ū/	baloney	/ē/ /ā/ /ĕ/ /o͞o/ /ū/
breakage	/ē/ /ā/ /ĕ/ /o͞o/ /ū/	chimney	/ē/ /ā/ /ĕ/ /o͞o/ /ū/

In working with vowel combinations, it is important to be flexible. Often a vowel sound can be spelled more than one way. First, learn the different ways a vowel sound can be spelled. Then if one spelling doesn't look right in a word, try another.

1 Circle the vowel combinations with *e* that say /ā/.

surveillance	breakable	obey	unveil
greatness	survey	neighbor	convey
freighter	weightless	beefsteak	reindeer

Four ways to spell /ā/ are _____, _____, _____, and _____.

2 Circle the vowel combinations with *e* that say /o͞o/ or /ū/.

euphemism	therapeutic	cashew	feudal
sewer	curfew	mildew	nephew
neutral	maneuver	Europe	jewel

Two ways to spell /o͞o/ and /ū/ are _____ and _____.

3 Circle the vowel combinations with *e* that say /ĕ/.

treachery	endeavor	instead	weather
ready	measure	pleasant	steady
breakfast	pleasure	feather	meadow

One way to spell /ĕ/ is _____.

4 Circle the vowel combinations with *e* that say /ē/.

protein	increase	volunteer	leisure
kidney	pedigree	journey	treaty
asleep	beneath	receive	money

Four ways to spell /ē/ are _____, _____, _____, and _____.

① Say each syllable, and then read the whole word. Underline the vowel combination with *e* in the whole word.

ee, ea, ey, ei = /ē/

free dom	freedom
a sleep	asleep
can teen	canteen
ref u gee	refugee
fea ture	feature
be neath	beneath
dis ease	disease
in crease	increase
kid ney	kidney
jock ey	jockey
at tor ney	attorney
ceil ing	ceiling
de ceive	deceive
caf feine	caffeine

ea = /ĕ/

read y	ready
break fast	breakfast
heath er	heather
in stead	instead
head quar ters	headquarters

ea, ei, ey, eigh = /ā/

great ly	greatly
break age	breakage
rein deer	reindeer
un veil	unveil
sur veil lance	surveillance
neigh bor hood	neighborhood
eight y	eighty
weight less	weightless
sur vey	survey
o bey	obey
con vey	convey
grey hound	greyhound

ew, eu = /o͞o/ or /ū/

jew el	jewel
cur few	curfew
feu dal	feudal
man eu ver	maneuver
ther a peu tic	therapeutic
neu tral i ty	neutrality

Practice Page 28ᴇ

1 Match the syllables to make real words. Say each word aloud as you write it.

be	son	_between_	pleas	ver	_____
rea	ew	_____	neu	stead	_____
sur	tween	_____	in	tral	_____
cash	vey	_____	bea	ant	_____

in	teen	_____	wea	bey	_____
val	crease	_____	o	ey	_____
fif	dow	_____	pro	pon	_____
mea	ley	_____	hock	tein	_____

teach	feine	_____	de	dew	_____
re	er	_____	tur	bor	_____
caf	er	_____	mil	gree	_____
sweat	peat	_____	neigh	key	_____

2 Unscramble the syllables to make real words.

teer   un   vol   _____

at   ney   tor   _____

hood   bor   neigh   _____

ceit   ed   con   _____

quar   ters   head   _____

lance   veil   sur   _____

i   tral   ty   neu   _____

ther   tic   a   peu   _____

① **Your teacher will dictate twenty-four words. Spell the missing syllable, using the hints at the left. Then say the whole word as you write it.**

/ē/—spelled *ee*

1. a _____   _____

2. em ploy _____   _____

3. dis a _____   _____

/ē/—spelled *ea*

4. _____ er   _____

5. _____ son   _____

6. re _____   _____

/ē/—spelled *ei*

7. pro _____   _____

8. _____ ther   _____

9. _____ ther   _____

/ē/—spelled *ey*

10. tur _____   _____

11. chim _____   _____

12. ba lo _____   _____

/ā/—spelled *ea*

13. _____ ly   _____

14. _____ age   _____

15. beef _____   _____

/ā/—spelled *ei*

16. _____ deer   _____

17. un _____   _____

18. sur _____ lance   _____

/ā/—spelled *eigh*

19. _____ ty   _____

20. _____ bor   _____

21. _____ less   _____

/ā/—spelled *ey*

22. o _____   _____

23. con _____   _____

24. sur _____   _____

⚙ Review

VC/CV	When two or more consonants stand between two vowels, divide between the consonants so that blends and digraphs stay together.
/Cle	Divide before the Consonant-*le*.
VV/	When a vowel combination appears at the end of a syllable, divide right after the vowel combination.
Compound Words	Divide between the two words.
Prefix/Root/Suffix	Divide between the prefix, root, and suffix (or ending).

(1) Divide these words into syllables using the VC/CV rule. Draw a box around the accented syllable.

chim|ney　　　curfew　　　canteen

committee　　　monkey　　　discreet

(2) Divide these words into syllables using the /Cle rule. Draw a box around the accented syllable.

measles　　　eagle

(3) Divide these words into syllables using the VV/ rule. Draw a box around the accented syllable.

reason　　　pewter　　　treaty

jewel　　　beaver　　　bleachers

(4) Divide these words into syllables using the compound words rule. Draw a box around the accented syllable.

greyhound　　　breakfast　　　beefsteak

(5) Divide these words into syllables using the prefix/root/suffix rule. Draw a box around the accented syllable.

release　　　breathless　　　protein

disease　　　greatest　　　unveil

---

ea

The vowel combination *ea* has three sounds:

> /ē/ as in *eat*   /ĕ/ as in *bread*   /ā/ as in *steak*

The following sentence will help you learn the sounds of *ea*: **Ea**t br**ea**d and st**ea**k.

---

① **Divide these words into syllables. Then write them under the correct headings.**

blea|chers	beefsteak	beaver	pleasant
measles	leather	greatest	pleasure
feature	steady	instead	squeamish
decrease	measure	peanut	breathless
breakable	ready	treaty	greatly

ea says /ē/ as in *eat*	*ea* says /ĕ/ as in *bread*	*ea* says /ā/ as in *steak*
bleachers		

② **QUICK CHECK** Have another student test you on spelling these words.

My score: ＿＿ / ＿＿ words correct

ei

The vowel combination *ei* has two sounds: /ē/ as in *seize* and /ā/ as in *veil*.

(1) Fill in the missing *ei,* and write the whole word. Then read the word aloud to practice the /ā/ sound.

_____ghteen   _____

r_____ndeer   _____

w_____ghtless   _____

fr_____ghter   _____

unv_____l   _____

surv_____llance   _____

ne_____ghbor   _____

(2) Fill in the missing *ei,* and write the whole word. Then read the word aloud to practice the /ē/ sound.

_____ther   _____

n_____ther   _____

l_____sure   _____

s_____zure   _____

prot_____n   _____

caff_____ne   _____

con_____ve   _____

/ā/

The /ā/ sound can be made by four vowel combinations with *e: ea, eigh, ey,* and *ei.*

ea says /ā/ in words such as *great, break,* and *steak.*

eigh says /ā/ in words such as *eight, neighbor, sleigh, weigh,* and *freight.*

ey says /ā/ in words such as *hey, they,* and *prey.*

ei says /ā/ in words such as *vein, veil, skein, rein,* and *feint.*

1 Fill in the missing vowel combination with *e* that makes the /ā/ sound. Then write the whole word.

gr_____hound   _____

_____ty   _____

_____teen   _____

beefst_____k   _____

surv_____   _____

ob_____   _____

gr_____tly   _____

r_____ndeer   _____

fr_____ter   _____

w_____tless   _____

unv_____l   _____

conv_____   _____

br_____kable   _____

surv_____llance   _____

2 **QUICK CHECK** Have another student test you on spelling some of these words.

My score: ____ /____ words correct

/ē/

The most common spelling of the /ē/ sound at the end of words is *y (happy, candy)*. However, *ee* and *ey* say /ē/ at the end of some words, too.

1 **Fill in the missing *ee* or *ey*, and then write the whole word.**

chimn_____   _____

disagr_____   _____

turk_____   _____

refug_____   _____

degr_____   _____

vall_____   _____

monk_____   _____

chimpanz_____   _____

all_____   _____

committ_____   _____

2 **Now write the words under the correct headings.**

ee	*ey*
_____	_____
_____	_____
_____	_____
_____	_____
_____	_____

3 **QUICK CHECK** Have another student test you on spelling these words.

My score: ____ /____ words correct

ew

The vowel combination *ew* has two sounds: /o͞o/ as in *mildew* and /ū/ as in *pewter*.
It can come at the end of a word or in the middle of a word.

1 **Fill in the missing *ew*, and then write the whole word.**

cash_____   _____

neph_____   _____

curf_____   _____

mild_____   _____

j_____el   _____

p_____ter   _____

s_____er   _____

eu

The sounds /o͞o/ or /ū/ can also be spelled *eu (neutral, feudal)*.
Words with *eu* may be difficult to spell. Many are Greek in origin.

2 **Read each word syllable by syllable. Then write the whole word and circle *eu*.**

neu tral   _____

ma neu ver   _____

neu tral i ty   _____

eu phor i a   _____

feu dal   _____

Eu rope   _____

ther a peu tic   _____

3 **QUICK CHECK Have another student test you on spelling some of these words.**

My score: ____ /____ words correct

1 Your teacher will dictate some words that contain vowel combinations with *e*. Repeat each word, listen for the vowel sound, and write the word under the correct heading.

/ē/ (spelled *ee, ea, ei,* or *ey*)

_____

_____

_____

_____

_____

_____

_____

_____

_____

_____

/ā/ (spelled *eigh, ey, ei,* or *ea*)

_____

_____

_____

_____

/ĕ/ (spelled *ea*)

_____

_____

_____

_____

/o͞o/ or /ū/ (spelled *ew* or *eu*)

_____

_____

1 Complete the puzzle with words from the box.

feudal	pedigree	treachery	conceal
endeavor	treatment	attorney	neutral
conceited	euphoria	discreet	euphemism

Across
2. self-centered; vain
5. a pleasant way of saying something, such as "pass away" instead of "die"
7. neither for nor against
8. a political system used in Europe during the Middle Ages
10. betrayal
11. another word for *lawyer*
12. medical care

Down
1. to try hard; to make a good effort
3. careful; cautious; showing good sense
4. to hide
6. a list of ancestors for a person or animal
9. extreme happiness

1 Fill in the blanks with words from the box.

caffeine	disease	peacock	eighty
bleachers	pheasants	weather	pleasant
sweater	neutral	employee	feathers

1. The _____ is getting cooler. Be sure to wear a

   _____ if you plan to go outside.

2. Four times twenty is _____.

3. The fans who were cheering and applauding the most sat in the

   _____.

4. Don't drink coffee before bed; it will keep you awake because it contains

   _____.

5. Ms. Bradley has been an _____ at the bank for

   three years and has no plans to leave any time soon.

6. Chicken pox is a childhood _____; it is much more severe

   if you catch it as an adult.

7. We had a _____ trip to the country, where we saw many

   _____ in a field.

8. The _____ is a beautiful bird that has many colorful tail

   _____.

9. I don't wish to take sides in this argument because I am friends with both of you.

   I will remain _____.

Proofreading Practice

Two of the List 28 words are misspelled in each sentence. Rewrite the whole sentence, and spell the words correctly.

1. When Heather had the meesles, she had a temperature of one hundred deegrees.

_____

_____

2. In our neaborhood there is a ten o'clock curfew for anyone under eiteen.

_____

_____

3. My nefew is on the committe that unveiled the new employee benefit plan.

_____

_____

4. The attorney and the teacher disagread over monney issues.

_____

_____

5. Are you ready for a walk through the medow in the vallee?

_____

_____

6. Betwean you and me, I'd rather play hockey insted of basketball.

_____

_____

7. Neighther employee was eeger to reason with Andrew.

_____

_____

8. We began our endevor with no money and meagre supplies.

_____

_____

(1) Read the sentences and circle all the List 28 words.

1. The thirteen refugees were asleep in the meadow.

2. My teacher was careful with the breakable teapot.

3. My neighbor, who is only eighteen, rode on the eighty-ton freighter.

4. The breathless runner was eager to measure how far she had run.

5. Uncle Andrew gave the jewel to his nephew.

6. The committee of volunteers should receive free tickets to the hockey game.

7. The weather was quite pleasant for our sailing endeavor.

8. Lewis wore a sweater even in warm weather.

9. Your waist size will increase greatly if you don't eat a good breakfast.

10. The employee with the squeamish stomach fainted when she saw the mildew.

11. My attorney offered me cashews and peanuts as I stepped into his office.

(2) Your teacher will dictate three of the sentences above. Write them on a blank piece of paper.

(3) Write a short story or descriptive paragraph using ten words from List 28. Be creative!

Reading & Spelling Skill Check

Demonstrate your accuracy in reading and spelling List 28 words. Your teacher will select ten words to read and ten words to spell. Record your scores on the Accuracy Checklist. Work toward 90–100 percent accuracy.

Word Proficiency

Now build up your reading proficiency with List 28 words. Decide on your rate goal with your teacher. Record your progress on the Word Proficiency Graph.

My goal for reading List 28 is _____ words per minute with two or fewer errors.

1 Practice the words, read the passage, and then answer the questions.

List 28 Words			Review Words		Passage Words
features	freedom	money	dollar	ideals	pyramid
eagle	between	instead	pictures	country	triangle
beneath	thirteen		unfinished	wisdom	symbolize
leaders	reason		United	future	symbol

History in Money

Have you ever looked closely at the back of a dollar bill? It features two pictures: a bald eagle and an unfinished pyramid beneath a triangle. These pictures are the front and back of the Great Seal of the United States. They symbolize the ideals of the first United States leaders and tell a story of the country's history.

The eagle is a symbol of freedom and strength. In between the eagle's head and tail is a shield with thirteen stripes, one for each of the first thirteen states.

The pyramid is also a symbol of strength. There is a reason that the pyramid is unfinished. It shows that the country is still growing. The eye within the triangle stands for skill and wisdom. It looks to the future, as a sign of hope.

The next time you look at a dollar bill, think of it as more than money. Instead, think of it as a small story in your hand.

1. Which word from the text means "has or includes"?_____

2. What is on the back of the U.S. dollar bill? _____

_____

3. Why is the pyramid in the Great Seal unfinished? _____

_____

2 FLUENCY Record your progress on the Fluency Graph.

My goal for reading the passage is _____ words per minute with two or fewer errors.

y = /ī/

analyze	humidify	recycle
ally	hyacinth	rely
apply	hybrid	reply
awry	hydrant	Ryan
beautify	hydrate	satisfy
carbohydrate	hydroelectric	solidify
certify	hydrogen	specify
clarify	hydroplane	stereotype
classify	hyena	stylish
cycle	hygiene	supply
cyclist	hyperactive	terrify
cyclone	hyphen	typewriter
cypress	hypothesis	typhoon
defy	identify	typing
dehydrate	imply	typist
deny	July	tyrant
dynamic	justify	unicycle
dynamite	magnify	Wyoming
dynamo	modify	
*dynasty	motorcycle	
encyclopedia	multiply	
enzyme	notify	
fortify	occupy	
fryer	pacify	
glorify	paralyze	
gratify	personify	
hereby	purify	
horrify	qualify	

y = /ĭ/

abyss	*symphony
analysis	symptom
anonymous	synonym
antonym	synthetic
bicycle	system
cryptic	tricycle
crystal	typical
cyclical	
cylinder	
cymbal	
cynic	
cynical	
dyslexia	
gymnastics	
hypnotize	
*mystery	
*mythology	
oxygen	
Pennsylvania	
physical	
sycamore	
syllable	
symbol	
symbolic	
symmetrical	
sympathetic	
sympathize	
*sympathy	

y = /ē/

- candy
- chemistry
- chilly
- Cindy
- city
- company
- copy
- easy
- emergency
- empty
- energy
- family
- fifty
- frenzy
- geography
- holly
- holy
- ivory
- Jenny
- Jeremy
- lady
- lazy
- library
- navy
- primary
- quantity
- twenty
- windy

* These words also contain the *y* sound /ē/.

In silent-*e* syllables, *y* says /ī/ as in *style*.

(1) **Below are some silent-*e* syllables found in List 29 words. Read these syllables aloud to practice the /ī/ sound.**

zyme   lyze   type

In closed syllables, *y* says /ĭ/ as in *gym*.

(2) **Below are some closed syllables found in List 29 words. Read these syllables aloud to practice the /ĭ/ sound.**

cyn   sym   hyp   phys   crys   dys

In open syllables, *y* can have two different sounds: /ī/ and /ē/.

(3) **Below are some open syllables found in List 29 words. Read these syllables aloud to practice the /ī/ and /ē/ sounds.**

y says /ī/			*y* says /ē/		
ny	hy	ply	dy	stry	zy
ry	fy	by	py	ty	vy

(4) **Spell two syllables in which *y* makes the following sounds:**

/ī/ _____ _____

/ĭ/ _____ _____

/ē/ _____ _____

The letter *y* usually has the same sounds as *i*. Use the chart to study the different vowel sounds *y* can make.

y says:

/ī/
- at the end of open syllables in the beginning, middle, or end of words *(hydrant, dehydrate, apply)*
- in silent-*e* syllables *(enzyme, analyze)*

/ĭ/
- in the middle of closed syllables *(system, hypnotize)*
- when it forms a syllable by itself *(oxygen, analysis)*

/ē/
- in open syllables at the end of some words *(twenty, library)*

(1) **Underline the *y* in each word, and circle the sound(s) *y* can make in that position.**

la dy	/ī/ /ĭ/ /ē/	
chil ly	/ī/ /ĭ/ /ē/	
sys tem	/ī/ /ĭ/ /ē/	
ty rant	/ī/ /ĭ/ /ē/	
hor ri fy	/ī/ /ĭ/ /ē/	
de ny	/ī/ /ĭ/ /ē/	
can dy	/ī/ /ĭ/ /ē/	
sup ply	/ī/ /ĭ/ /ē/	
mag ni fy	/ī/ /ĭ/ /ē/	
de hy drate	/ī/ /ĭ/ /ē/	

an a lyze	/ī/ /ĭ/ /ē/
li brar y	/ī/ /ĭ/ /ē/
dy na mite	/ī/ /ĭ/ /ē/
an to nym	/ī/ /ĭ/ /ē/
par a lyze	/ī/ /ĭ/ /ē/
syn thet ic	/ī/ /ĭ/ /ē/
mul ti ply	/ī/ /ĭ/ /ē/
chem is try	/ī/ /ĭ/ /ē/
Wy o ming	/ī/ /ĭ/ /ē/
oc cu py	/ī/ /ĭ/ /ē/

1 Say each syllable, and then read the whole word. Underline the *y* in the whole word.

y = /ē/ (end of words)

la dy	lady
ho ly	holy
na vy	navy
win dy	windy
emp ty	empty
la zy	lazy
li brar y	library
i vor y	ivory
fam i ly	family

y = /ī/ (end of words)

de ny	deny
de fy	defy
re ply	reply
Ju ly	July
sup ply	supply
pac i fy	pacify
mul ti ply	multiply
oc cu py	occupy
no ti fy	notify

y = /ī/ (open syllables)

cy press	cypress
hy phen	hyphen
ty rant	tyrant
de hy drate	dehydrate
car bo hy drate	carbohydrate

y = /ī/ (silent-*e* syllables)

en zyme	enzyme
an a lyze	analyze
par a lyze	paralyze
ster e o type	stereotype

y = /ĭ/ (closed syllables and whole syllables)

sym bol	symbol
sys tem	system
syl la ble	syllable
cyn ic	cynic
a byss	abyss
typ i cal	typical
an to nym	antonym
dys lex i a	dyslexia
ox y gen	oxygen
a nal y sis	analysis
a non y mous	anonymous

1 Match the syllables to make real words. Say each word as you write it.

twen	y	_twenty_		al	ny	_____
cop	ty	_____		de	ry	_____
win	zy	_____		aw	by	_____
fren	dy	_____		here	ply	_____
ho	ly	_____		ap	ly	_____

cyn	bal	_____		fry	cle	_____
sym	tal	_____		ty	lish	_____
cym	tem	_____		sty	drant	_____
sys	ic	_____		hy	rant	_____
crys	bol	_____		cy	er	_____

2 Unscramble the syllables to make real words.

pa thy sym	_____
try chem is	_____
y vor i	_____
nas tics gym	_____
o myth gy ol	_____
y sis nal a	_____
fy i qual	_____
sis e poth hy	_____
no hyp tize	_____
drate hy de	_____

1) Your teacher will dictate fifteen words. Spell the missing syllable(s). Then say the whole word as you write it under the correct heading. Two of the words have two *y's* in them and should be classified in two ways.

1. _____ cu _____

2. la _____

3. _____ ty

4. sup _____

5. de _____

6. _____ brar _____

7. _____ ter _____

8. _____ ni _____

9. _____ _____ ti _____

10. _____ thet _____

11. _____ la   ble

12. _____ _____ lyze

13. par _____ _____

14. _____ nas _____

15. _____ ol   o _____

y says /ī/	*y* says /ē/	*y* says /ĭ/
_____	_____	_____
_____	_____	_____
_____	_____	_____
_____	_____	_____
_____	_____	_____
_____		

-ify

The common two-syllable ending *-ify* is pronounced /ĭ fī´/. The primary accent is always on the syllable just before *-ify,* but *fy* has a secondary accent.

(1) Draw a box around the syllable with the primary accent and underline *fy*. Then write the whole word.

grat i fy	*gratify*	spec i fy	_____
class i fy	_____	ter ri fy	_____
jus ti fy	_____	clar i fy	_____
for ti fy	_____	hor ri fy	_____
cer ti fy	_____	pur i fy	_____
glor i fy	_____	beau ti fy	_____
mod i fy	_____	qual i fy	_____
mag ni fy	_____	pac i fy	_____
i den ti fy	_____	hu mid i fy	_____
so lid i fy	_____	per son i fy	_____

(2) Fill in the blanks with *-ify* words from Activity 1.

1. If the room does not have enough moisture, please _____ it.

2. Cheating is wrong at any time; you cannot _____ it.

3. I did not _____ for the scholarship because of my low grades.

4. He could not _____ the suspect in the police lineup.

5. The city had to _____ the water before people could drink it.

6. The monster movie was designed to _____ and _____ the audience.

7. A microscope is used to _____ very small objects.

The letter *y* can say /ī/ or /ē/ at the end of multisyllabic words. If you read a word with a *y* ending that you do not know, sound it out, giving *y* the /ī/ sound first. If that does not make a recognizable word, try the /ē/ sound.

1 Circle /ī/ or /ē/ to tell what sound *y* makes in each word. Then write each word syllable by syllable under the correct heading.

occupy	/ī/ /ē/	energy	/ī/ /ē/	supply	/ī/ /ē/
imply	/ī/ /ē/	deny	/ī/ /ē/	satisfy	/ī/ /ē/
Cindy	/ī/ /ē/	fifty	/ī/ /ē/	empty	/ī/ /ē/
July	/ī/ /ē/	quantity	/ī/ /ē/	lazy	/ī/ /ē/
magnify	/ī/ /ē/	reply	/ī/ /ē/	multiply	/ī/ /ē/
geography	/ī/ /ē/	navy	/ī/ /ē/	emergency	/ī/ /ē/
frenzy	/ī/ /ē/	qualify	/ī/ /ē/		

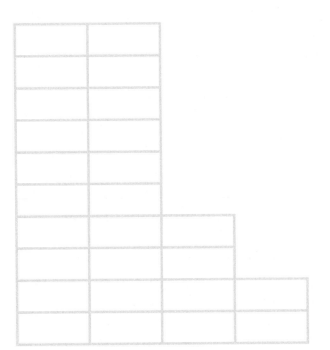

y says /ē/

y says /ī/

When you see *y* in the middle of a word,
- it could be at the end of an open syllable and say /ī/ *(hy drant)*.
- it could be in a closed syllable and say /ĭ/ *(sys tem)*.

① Divide each word into syllables. Then mark the *y* syllable as closed (C) or open (O), and circle the sound *y* makes as /ī/ or /ĭ/.

	Type of Syllable	Sound of *y*		Type of Syllable	Sound of *y*
c y|c l e	O	(/ī/) /ĭ/	s t y l i s h	_____	/ī/ /ĭ/
c y l i n d e r	_____	/ī/ /ĭ/	c r y s t a l	_____	/ī/ /ĭ/
t y r a n t	_____	/ī/ /ĭ/	h y b r i d	_____	/ī/ /ĭ/
s y m b o l	_____	/ī/ /ĭ/	s y n t h e t i c	_____	/ī/ /ĭ/
t y p i c a l	_____	/ī/ /ĭ/	d y n a m o	_____	/ī/ /ĭ/
t y p h o o n	_____	/ī/ /ĭ/	c y n i c a l	_____	/ī/ /ĭ/
h y p h e n	_____	/ī/ /ĭ/	h y p o t h e s i s	_____	/ī/ /ĭ/
p h y s i c a l	_____	/ī/ /ĭ/	h y p n o t i z e	_____	/ī/ /ĭ/
c r y p t i c	_____	/ī/ /ĭ/	a n t o n y m	_____	/ī/ /ĭ/
h y g i e n e	_____	/ī/ /ĭ/	d y n a m i t e	_____	/ī/ /ĭ/

② Read the definitions. Choose the correct word from Activity 1, and write it on the line.

a mixture of two different things _____

to put someone in a trance _____

made by artificial means _____

an explosive _____

a cruel or unjust ruler _____

a long, round object _____

a tropical storm _____

1 Common patterns with *y* vowels are illustrated below. Add the pattern to the word, and then write the whole word as you read it aloud.

Add *dyna* _____ mo _____

_____ mite _____

_____ sty _____

_____ mic _____

Add *sym* _____ pathy _____

_____ bol _____

_____ metrical _____

_____ ptom _____

_____ phony _____

Add *hy* _____ drant _____

_____ phen _____

_____ brid _____

_____ giene _____

_____ pothesis _____

Add *ty* _____ phoon _____

_____ rant _____

_____ pist _____

_____ pewriter _____

2 **QUICK CHECK** Have another student test you on spelling these words.

My score: ____ / ____ words correct

1 Your teacher will dictate twenty words. Repeat each syllable, and then say the whole word as you write it.

y says /ē/ at the end of words

1. _____
2. _____
3. _____
4. _____
5. _____

y says /ī/ at the end of words

6. _____
7. _____
8. _____
9. _____
10. _____

y says /ī/ in open syllables

11. _____
12. _____
13. _____
14. _____
15. _____

y says /ĭ/ in closed syllables

16. _____
17. _____
18. _____
19. _____
20. _____

Hydro (hydr-) is a Greek root that means "water."

1 **Read the definitions. Choose the correct word from the box, and write it on the line.**

> hydroplane   hydroelectric   hydrogen
> hydrate   dehydrate   hydrant

a gas that combines with oxygen to make water   _____

to cause to absorb water   _____

producing electricity with water power   _____

to cause to lose lots of water   _____

a pipe that dispenses water when a hose is attached   _____

a boat that skims above the water's surface   _____

Cycle (cycl-) is a Greek root that means "circle," "a recurring time period," or "wheel."

2 **Read the definitions. Choose the correct word from the box, and write it on the line.**

> cycle   bicycle   unicycle   cyclist
> recycle   cyclone   motorcycle

a violent storm with strong winds   _____

a person who rides a cycle   _____

a vehicle with two wheels   _____

a recurring time period   _____

a vehicle with two wheels and a motor   _____

to process something so that it can be used again   _____

a vehicle with one wheel   _____

(1) **Fill in the blanks with words from the box.**

synonyms	cryptic	justify	cynical
abyss	paralyzed	multiply	analyze
cypress	dyslexia	occupy	encyclopedia

1. Chemists _____ chemicals to find out what they are made of.

2. A _____ message is mysterious and hard to figure out.

3. The words *pretty* and *beautiful* are _____.

4. Jeremy had no excuse; he could not _____ his foolish actions.

5. Jenny looked at an online _____ to get information about Spain.

6. The man was _____ after his neck was injured.

7. Cindy could add and subtract, but she had not yet learned to

   _____ or divide.

8. The _____ tree is in the evergreen family.

9. People with _____ have difficulty learning to read.

10. Two objects cannot _____ the same space at the same time.

11. When the mountain climber fell into the _____, it took

    days to rescue him.

12. A _____ remark is one that expresses distrust about a

    person's motives.

✂️ **Proofreading Practice**

Two of the List 29 words are misspelled in each sentence. Rewrite the whole sentence, and spell the words correctly.

1. Please notifi the cyclysts that our supply of helmets is running low.

_____

_____

2. It was easy for Ryan to learn to multiplie, but he was too lazy to learn jeography.

_____

_____

3. The tipicle familye takes a week's vacation in July.

_____

_____

4. Did the repliy to your letter satisfie you, or did it only magnify your anger?

_____

_____

5. Jenny did not have enough energy to ride her bicicle to the lybrarie.

_____

_____

6. I have no simpathy for people who classify themselves as synical.

_____

_____

7. To modify your motorcycul, you will need to spessify what kind of bike it is.

_____

_____

8. In kemistry, scientists analyz both natural and synthetic substances.

_____

_____

(1) **Read the sentences and circle all the List 29 words.**

1. The cryptic note was anonymous; who wrote it was a mystery to Cindy.

2. The bird flew from the cypress to the holly to the sycamore tree.

3. In chemistry, water is described as being two parts hydrogen and one part oxygen.

4. The family had to notify their neighbors that they were leaving.

5. The tyrant made cruel threats to terrify the subjects of his city.

6. Jenny and Jeremy were the stars in their physical education and gymnastics classes.

7. The train took us from Wyoming to Pennsylvania.

8. I tried to identify the pieces that the symphony played, but they were not your typical pieces.

9. Ryan did not qualify for Navy supply school.

10. Could you please specify what kind of bicycle you want to buy?

(2) **Your teacher will dictate three of the sentences above. Write them on a blank piece of paper.**

(3) **Write a short story or descriptive paragraph using ten words from List 29. Be creative!**

Reading & Spelling Skill Check

Demonstrate your accuracy in reading and spelling List 29 words. Your teacher will select ten words to read and ten words to spell. Record your scores on the Accuracy Checklist. Work toward 90–100 percent accuracy.

Word Proficiency

Now build up your reading proficiency with List 29 words. Decide on your rate goal with your teacher. Record your progress on the Word Proficiency Graph.

My goal for reading List 29 is _____ words per minute with two or fewer errors.

1 Practice the words, read the passage, and then answer the questions.

List 29 Words			Review Words		Passage Words
hydrogen	supply	oxygen	fuel	money	scientists
primary	rely	easy	future	abundant	enough
energy	satisfy	fifty	pollution	power	electricity

Hydrogen: Fuel of the Future?

Oil is our primary source of energy. But burning oil causes lots of pollution. It also costs a lot of money, and the supply is running out. We cannot rely on this type of energy forever.

Many scientists think hydrogen will satisfy our energy needs. Hydrogen is abundant and bonds with oxygen to form water. Hydrogen's fuel cells don't cause pollution, and they make enough electricity to power cars and heat homes.

Switching to hydrogen will not be easy. Making hydrogen fuel cells can be costly. Plus, electricity is required to get the hydrogen out of water, and right now most electricity still comes from burning oil.

Iceland is hard at work switching over to hydrogen. In fifty years, it hopes to rely mostly on hydrogen—not oil—for fuel. Over time, could hydrogen become the fuel of the future?

1. Which word from the text means "count on"? _____

2. What are two reasons why hydrogen might be a good fuel source?_____

   _____

3. Why will switching to hydrogen not be easy?_____

   _____

2 **FLUENCY** Record your progress on the Fluency Graph.

My goal for reading the passage is _____ words per minute with two or fewer errors.

abyss	corduroy	endeavor	neutral
alphabet	country	entertain	obey
altitude	couple	essay	occupy
analysis	cyclone	Europe	protein
announce	cynic	exploit	raccoon
antonym	dawdle	frenzy	receipt
appoint	degree	hydrogen	reindeer
audience	deny	increase	satisfy
augment	discreet	laundry	sausage
automatic	distraught	leisure	shallow
awkward	drowsy	library	sympathy
cashew	elbow	magnify	trousers
charcoal	embroider	maintain	typhoon
cocoa	emergency	measles	walnut
complain	employ	mystery	weapon

1 Match the syllables to make real words. Say each word aloud as you write it.

a	ny	_abyss_	es	ment	_____
cy	zy	_____	laun	say	_____
de	byss	_____	aug	traught	_____
ty	clone	_____	dis	dle	_____
fren	phoon	_____	daw	dry	_____

co	low	_____	pro	bey	_____
em	sy	_____	o	tein	_____
cou	ploy	_____	rein	crease	_____
shal	coa	_____	neu	tral	_____
drow	ple	_____	in	deer	_____

2 Unscramble the syllables to make real words.

y sym path _____

ti al tude _____

deav en or _____

em der broi _____

bet al pha _____

gen dro hy _____

ni fy mag _____

ter en tain _____

to au ic mat _____

gen e cy mer _____

3 Fill in the blanks with words from the box.

charcoal	cocoa	neutral	sausages
cashews	announce	satisfy	trousers
embroider	degrees	maintain	emergency

1. Darla drank a thermos of hot _____ to keep warm when the

   temperature dropped below 30 _____ Fahrenheit.

2. Rather than _____ whose side you are on, try to remain

   _____ when friends have an argument.

3. At the ball park, the vendor cooked hot dogs and _____

   on his _____ grill.

4. In order to _____ your hunger, why don't you eat some

   walnuts, _____, or another light snack?

5. I tried to _____ my corduroy _____

   with a flower pattern, but I only ended up ruining them.

6. I try to _____ my calm even in the event of an

   _____.

Proofreading Practice

Two of the Review List words are misspelled in each sentence. Cross out each misspelled word, and write the correct spelling above it.

1. I like to occupy my leasure time reading mystery books from the libraree.

2. Roy endevored to entertain the audience by telling them of his exployts in Europe.

3. The doctor's analysis is that you don't have meesles, so please don't complayne.

4 Complete the puzzle with words from the box.

weapon	discreet	awkward	raccoon
antonym	elbow	cynic	country
magnify	appoint	receipt	obey

Across
  1. not graceful
  5. to assign someone a job
  7. a person who has a negative outlook
  9. arm joint
  10. a word that is the opposite of another
  12. careful; cautious

Down
  2. object used to cause harm
  3. a small gray animal with a ringed tail
  4. to make greater; to increase in size
  6. a printed statement of a transaction
  8. opposite of *city*
  11. to do as one is told

Vowel Combination Patterns

Sounds

Vowel Combinations	/o͞o/, /ū/	/ō/	/ow/	/oi/	/ŭ/, /ə/	/ā/	/aw/	/ē/	/ĕ/	/all/	/ăl/
oa		cocoa									
ow		window	flower								
oi				poison							
oy				royal							
oo	balloon										
ou	routine		county		cousin famous						
ai						detail					
ay						rayon					
au							laundry				
aw							awful				
augh							daughter				
al										walnut	alphabet
ee								asleep			
ea						breakable		teacher	feather		
ei						unveil		receive			
ey						obey		turkey			
eigh						eighty					
ew	jewel										
eu	neutral										

Megawords 5, Lists 26–29

Name _____

Word List	Examples	Check Test Scores Date:		Reading Skill Check			Spelling Skill Check		
		Reading	Spelling						
26. Vowel Combinations with *o*	acoustic shallow								
27. Vowel Combinations with *a*	nautical mayor								
Review List: 26–27									
28. Vowel Combinations with *e*	neutrality endeavor								
29. Vowel Sounds of *y*	oxygen cyclone								
Review List: 26–29									

Record scores as fractions: $\dfrac{\text{\# correct}}{\text{\# attempted}}$

Word Proficiency Graph

Name _____

Goal _____

•———• Words read correctly in one minute (WCPM)

✕———✕ Errors

WCPM

80
70
60
50
40
30
20
10

Errors

0

Word List* _____
Date _____
Errors _____
WCPM** _____

* Repeat Word Lists as many times as needed.

**Word Count Per Minute (WCPM) = Words read in one minute - Errors

Word Proficiency Graph

Name _____

Goal _____

●————● Words read correctly in one minute (WCPM)

✗————✗ Errors

WCPM

80

70

60

50

40

30

20

10

Errors

0

Word List* _____

Date _____

Errors _____

WCPM** _____

* Repeat Word Lists as many times as needed.

**Word Count Per Minute (WCPM) = Words read in one minute - Errors

Fluency Graph

Name _____

Goal _____

●———● Words read correctly in one minute (WCPM)

✕———✕ Errors

WCPM

160

140

120

100

80

60

40

20

Errors

0

Passage* _____

Date _____

Errors _____

WCPM** _____

* Repeat Passages as many times as needed.

**Word Count Per Minute (WCPM) = Words read in one minute - Errors

EXAMINER'S RECORDING FORM — READING

Check Test: Word Lists 26–29
Megawords 5

Name _____ Date _____

26. Vowel Combinations with *o*

kangaroo

window

approach

mountain

embroider

correct _____

27. Vowel Combinations with *a*

entertain

laundry

unlawful

walrus

altitude

correct _____

28. Vowel Combinations with *e*

employee

endeavor

neighbor

leisure

maneuver

correct _____

29. Vowel Sounds of *y*

cyclone

magnify

hypnotize

ivory

analysis

correct _____

Total Correct _____

Total Possible __20__

EXAMINER'S RECORDING FORM — READING

Name _____   Date _____

26.   Vowel Combinations with o

kangaroo

window

approach

mountain

embroider

correct _____

27.   Vowel Combinations with a

entertain

laundry

unlawful

walrus

altitude

correct _____

28.   Vowel Combinations with e

employee

endeavor

neighbor

leisure

maneuver

correct _____

29.   Vowel Sounds of y

cyclone

magnify

hypnotize

ivory

analysis

correct _____

Total Correct _____

Total Possible _____ *20*